Mr Blobby's Joke Book

Joke Book

Radio Times *Readers' Favourite Blobby Jokes*

BBC CHILDREN'S BOOKS

Published by BBC Children's Books,
a division of BBC Enterprises Limited,
Woodlands, 80 Wood Lane,
London W12 0TT

First published 1994

ISBN 0 563 40341 1

Typeset by BBC Children's Books
Printed and bound by Clays Ltd, St Ives plc

Mr Blobby's Joke Book

When *Radio Times* ran a competition for Britain's best Blobby jokes, Mr Blobby was overwhelmed by the response . . . tickled pink in fact. The chortling could be heard throughout Crinkley Bottom as he worked through the entries and made the selection of winning jokes.

Condolences if you sent in an entry and it didn't make the joke book. If your joke is included, congratulations! The names of the prizewinners are listed at the back of the book.

We hope you'll agree with Mr Blobby that this collection of his jokes knocks the blobs off any others!

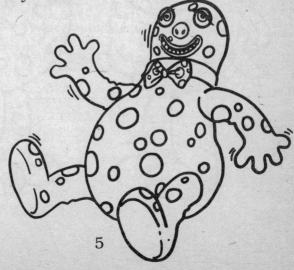

Who clears the drains at The Great House in Crinkley Bottom?
The odd blob man.

What did Mrs Blobby say when she saw Mr Blobby's new bow tie?
'You look a right blobby dazzler!'

Who's pink, yellow and green, and
hides in Sherwood Forest?
Blobbin Hood.

Who is Crinkley Bottom's MP?
Virginia Blobbomly.

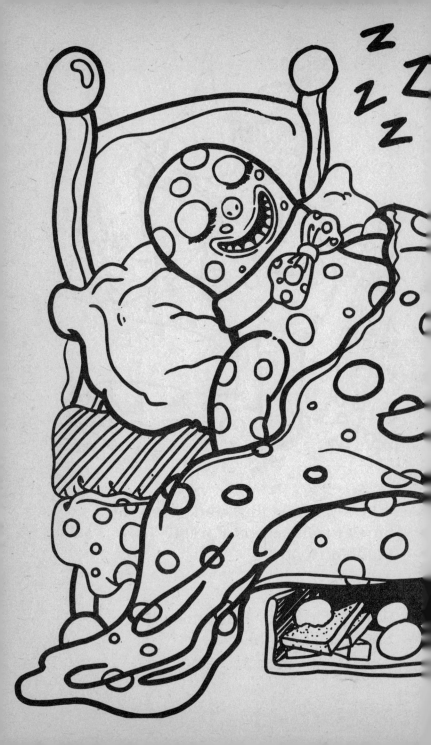

What does Mr Blobby keep in a box
under his bed?
Bits and blobs.

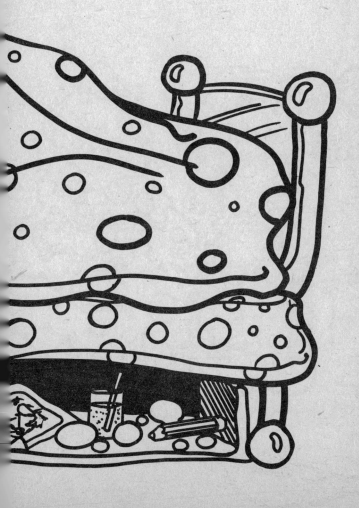

Who killed Roger Rabbit?
Blob Hoskins.

How does the Blobby family decorate
its Christmas tree?
With blobbles.

What's huge and eats pink and yellow
cavemen?
Blobbysaurus.

What does Mrs Blobby wear on her
feet?
Blobby sox.

What do you give Mr Blobby if he's feeling seasick?
Plenty of room!

What car does Mr Blobby drive?
A Blobbin Reliant.

Who is Mr Blobby's royal Scottish
ancestor?
Blobby Prince Charlie.

'Mr Blobby broke his leg yesterday
while he was picking apples.'
'That's terrible. What did
Mrs Blobby do?'
'She opened a can of peaches!'

How did Dick Turpin make a living?
Highway blobbery.

What did Mr Blobby give Mrs Blobby
on their wedding anniversary?
A bunch of blobelias.

Where does the Blobby family go
on holiday?
Blobnor Regis.

16

How would you feel if you ate six melons, five bowls of custard and four large plates of blancmange? *Melanblobby.*

What goes bounce blob, bounce blob? *Mr Blobby rolling downhill.*

What's pink with yellow spots and goes
up and down?
Mr Blobby in a lift.

On which day would Mr Blobby's
bow tie normally be seen?
On Sir Blobbin Day.

What does Grandad Blobby
use for money?
Ten blob notes.

Why did the Crinkley Bottom farmer smile when he fell over in a field full of cowpats?
Because he'd just missed a blobby!

What's pink with size twelve feet?
The blobby on the beat.

Why is Mr Blobby a very good
neighbour?
*Because he's always blobbing in and
out to see you.*

Blobby had a little lamb,
It had a touch of colic,
He gave it brandy twice a day
And now it's alcoholic!

What are pink with yellow spots and
live on the seabed?
Blobsters.

What does Mr Blobby put in his
bathwater?
Himself.

What are Mr Blobby's favourite books?

The BFG – Blobby Feels Great
Blobinson Crusoe
The Blobbit
The Collected Poems of Blobbie Burns

What's pink with yellow spots and keeps your ears warm?
A blobble hat.

How does Mrs Blobby have her
hair done?
In a blob.

What's round, pink and yellow and
tastes of aniseed?
A blobstopper.

What do you call pink biscuits with
yellow spots?
Blobnobs.

Who took the Crinkley Bottom
international squad to the semi-finals
of the 1990 World Cup?
Blobby Robson.

What was the front page news of last
week's *Crinkley Bottom Gazette*?
Armed bank blobbery.

Why is Mr Blobby always happy?
Because he's tickled pink.

What do you get if you cross Mr Blobby
with a cow?
A spotty pink milkshake.

Why did Mr Blobby go to Oxford?
To visit the Blobleian library.

Why does Mr Blobby's dog have such
a shiny nose?
*Because he takes his Blob Martins
every day.*

When is your car washed by something
pink wearing a woggle?
Blob-a-job week.

Mrs Blobby couldn't start her car, so
Mr Blobby said he would try for her.
'I'm sorry,' said Mr Blobby, 'the
battery's flat.'
'Oh dear,' Mrs Blobby replied.
'What shape should it be?'

Why did Mr Blobby put a cow in his garden?
Because he wanted a lawnmooer.

Why did Mr Blobby call his guard dog Ginger?
Because Ginger snaps!

Where does Professor Blobby carry out his experiments?
In the lablobbytory.

Why did Mr Blobby throw away
his keys?
*Because being bald he didn't have
any locks.*

Why has Mr Blobby got a hole in
his head?
He's had a blobotomy.

Why did Mr Blobby go to a nightclub?
Because he wanted a job as a bouncer.

Who's pink with yellow spots and
controls the programmes on BBC1?
Alan Yentblob.

What disease swept through Crinkley
Bottom in the fourteenth century?
Blobbonic plague.

Why did Noel Edmonds yell with pain?
He'd just been stung by a blobbee!

What happens to Mr Blobby if he stays in the bath too long?
He gets a Crinkley Bottom!

What's pink with yellow spots and digs up graves?
A blobby snatcher.

Who gives the weather forecasts in
Crinkley Bottom?
Blob Rust.

What's pink and yellow and read
all over?
'The Blobserver'.

Why didn't Mr Blobby join the SAS?
Because he couldn't get round the blobstacle course.

In which film is Madonna Mr Blobby's leading lady?
'Blobby of Evidence'.

Who's a cracker in Crinkley Bottom?
Blobby Coltrane.

Who's pink with yellow spots
and plays chess?
Blobby Fischer.

What's pink and spotty and provides
the 'future of law enforcement'?
Roboblob.

Who is Mr Blobby's favourite pianist?
Blobby Crush.

Why did Mr Blobby want to call his
baby 'Six-and-seven-eighths'?
He picked the name out of a hat.

What's pink and bouncy and makes
people laugh with impersonations?
Blobby Davro.

Who rode the winning horse in the
Crinkley Bottom Derby?
Blob Champion.

How does Mr Blobby keep in shape?
*He goes blobby building down at
the gym.*

Who's pink and yellow and had a hit
with *Nessun Dorma?*
Luciano Blobberotti.

Which Italian gangster organizes the
Mafia in Crinkley Bottom?
The Blobfather.

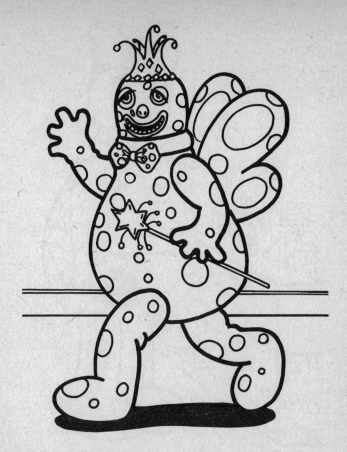

Which part will Mr Blobby be playing
when Crinkley Bottom Amateur
Dramatic Club puts on the pantomime
'Cinderella'?
The Fairy Blobmother.

Who's pink and doesn't like Mondays?
Blob Geldof.

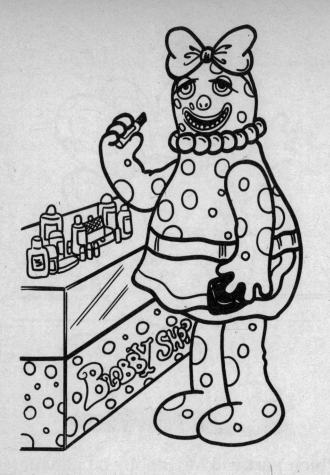

Where does Mrs Blobby buy her beauty products?
The Blobby Shop.

Where would you find gainful employment in Crinkley Bottom?
In the Blob Centre.

What's the favourite wild animal in
Crinkley Bottom zoo?
The blobcat.

'Did you know that Mr Blobby works
for the Queen?'
'No, what does he do?'
'He's her personal blobbyguard!'

Why did Mr Blobby go to the House of Commons?
To blobby his MP.

Why did Mr Blobby stick his feet in a bowl of jelly?
Because he wanted a pair of gum boots.

What does Snobby Blobby have on his
mantelpiece?
Expensive 'blobjets d'art'.

Who starred with Bing Crosby in the
film *The Road to Mandalay*?
Blob Hope.

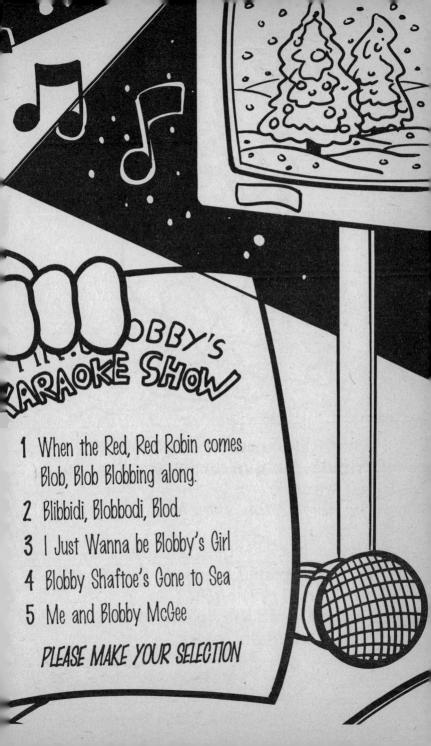

What frightened the residents of
Crinkley Bottom during a cold snap
last winter?
The ablobinable snowman.

What happened when Mr Blobby fell
off the end of the pier?
*Nothing much. He just blobbed up
and down in the water.*

Who is Tiny Tim's father?
Blob Cratchitt.

Who are pink with yellow spots and
catch criminals in Gotham City?
Batman and Blobbin.

What would you say if you were charged £2.50 for a cuppa in the Crinkley Bottom Tearoom?
'It's daylight blobbery!'

Where does Mr Blobby have his shoes mended?
At the blobbler.

What's Mr Blobby's fastest swimming stroke?
The blobby paddle.

What could Noel Edmonds see through his telescope?
A blob on the landscape.

Why does Mr Blobby keep falling off his bicycle?
Because all the roads in Crinkley Bottom are paved with blobblestones.

What language does Mr Blobby speak?
Blobbledygook.

How did Mr Blobby propose to
Mrs Blobby?
He got down on one knee and said,
'I don't need noblobby but you'.

Why does Mr Blobby eat so many
mushrooms?
*Because they make him a fungi to
be with!*

What Hallowe'en tradition takes place
in Crinkley Bottom every year?
Blobbing for apples.

Who's pink and yellow
and blowing in the wind?
Blob Dylan.

What new role is Mrs Blobby playing in the Crinkley Bottom community?
Lolliblob lady.

Who shot the sherrif in Crinkley Bottom (but didn't shoot the deputy)?
Blob Marley and the Wailers.

Who's pink with yellow spots and married to your auntie?
Blob's your uncle.

Why couldn't Mr Blobby go to the disco?
Because he had no blobby to go with.

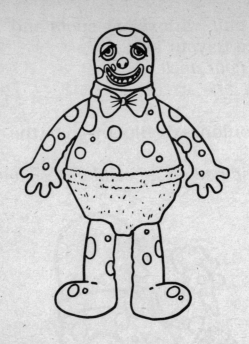

What does Baby Blobby want for Christmas?
A blobby horse.

What are Mr Blobby's favourite TV shows?

Rag, Tag and Blobtail
Thunderblobs
Blobbusters with Blob Holness
Blobbety Blob
Blob's Full House with Blob Monkhouse

MR BLOBBY'S CAFE

on the menu today . . .

Breakfast Cereal
Snap, crackle and blob

Starter
Corn on the blob

Fish Course
Blobster Thermidor

Italian Special
Spaghetti Blobognese

Mrs Blobby's
Good Home Cooking Set Menu
Blobble and squeak
followed by
Blobbery Pie *or* Syllablob

Winners

Janet Armer
of Cockerham,
Lancaster

Alex Browne
of Wimbledon

Matthew Best
of Chiddingfold,
Surrey

Hannah Best
of Chiddingfold,
Surrey

Madeleine Bristow
of Wirksworth,
Derbyshire

Miss H.R. Westcott
of Tuffley, Gloucester

Mrs J. Crowther
of Huddersfield

Philip Lawrence
of Lowestoft

Jennifer Crossley
of Trowbridge

**Rebecca and
Jemma Willis**
of Nottingham

Jimpy Mendham
of Waltham Forest,
London

Zoe Smale
of Watford,

**Bartholomew Fallon
Johnson**
of St Day, Cornwall

Lauren Cooper
of Aberdeen

Annie Riley
of Warrington

Elliott Pearson
of Liverpool

Christopher Granite
of Arlesey, Beds

Heather Griffiths
of Thame,
Oxfordshire

Felicity Eykyn
of Solihull

**Miss Catherine
Hope**
of Huddersfield

Hilary Biggs
of Winchmore Hill,
London

Paul Tilston
of Chester

Jonathon Holland
of Beccles, Suffolk

Alfie Hillman
of Lowestoft

Isabelle Bristow
of Wirksworth,
Derbyshire

Giles Willey
of Letchworth, Herts

Mrs Susan Davies
of Wrexham

Martin James
of Chatham

Pauline Trusselle
of Birmingham

Rupert Wright
of Aboyne,
Aberdeenshire

Geraldine Straker
of Winsford, Cheshire

Samantha Hannam
of Folkstone

Sam Davies
of Penarth, South
Glamorgan

Julian Lucy
of South Godstone,
Surrey

Ashley Garner
of Basildon

G. Davis
of Bristol

Mrs G. Morgan
of Penshurst, Kent

Neil Walden
of Linton, Cambs

Kelly Ford
of Bradford

Amy Broadhead
of York

**Amy and
James Firth**
of Fen Drayton,
Cambridgeshire

Miss V. Redhall
of Bristol

Mrs A. Thresher
of Bristol

Mr N. Janas
of Bristol

C. Bellot
of Gravesend

Andrew Cecil
of Chelmsford

Luke Edwards
of Solihull

Diana Taylor
of Southampton

Sian Davies
of Llandudno

Mark Dent
of Cirencester

Leanne Davies
of Holywell, Clwyd

Charlotte Jackson
of Congleton,
Cheshire

M. A. Cowgill
of Salford

Mrs C. Skelton
of Bristol

Colin Cripps
of Leyton, London

Robert Wilkinson
of Willesden, London

Susan Robbins
of Middleton-on-Sea,
West Sussex

Mark Fall
of Scarborough

David Collett
of Bristol

Robert Line
of Warrington

Helen Taylor
of Plymouth

Nicola Morgan
of Blackpool

Sally Taylor
of Rochdale

Tina-Jo O'Neill
of New Brighton,
Wirral

Alison Gibson
of Carlisle

Alice Godley
of Congleton,
Cheshire

Richard Evans
of Bath

Camilla Talbot
of Brighton

Nick Watson
of Ealing, London

Alex Simmonds
of Rayleigh, Essex

S. Baylis
of Malvern, Worcs

Lucy Marsh
of Newmarket

Mike Leader
of London

Peter Kinnersley
of London

Jodie Crossland
of Bradford

Elinor Wood
of Hornchurch, Essex

Karen Moses
of St Leonards-on-
Sea, East Sussex

Mr K. Nunn
of Ilford, Essex

Luke Kemp
of St Helier, Jersey

Alice Pursglove
of Sheffield

Olive Hall
of Ashbourne,
Derbyshire

Charlie Stroud
of Brighton

Tracey Williams
of Coedpoeth, Clwyn

Beverly Gooding
of Sleaford, Lincs

Michelle and Allister Collins
of Redbourn,
Hertfordshire

Fiona Waters
of Ferndown, Dorset

Casey Matthews
of London

Richard Farrage
of Gateshead, Tyne
and Wear

Natasha Matejtshuk
of Hitchin, Hertford

L. Melville
of Edinburgh

Chris Campbell
of Newcastle-upon-
Tyne

D. Mason
of Durham

Julie Grafton
of Coventry

David Barber
of Hoddesdon, Herts

Lucy Hill
of St Helens,
Merseyside

Paula Reid
of Aberdeen

Caroline Beaverstock
of Bath

Glyn Boxall
of Spalding,
Lincolnshire

Michael Gates
of Shoreham-by-Sea,
West Sussex

Samantha Borrowman
of Flint